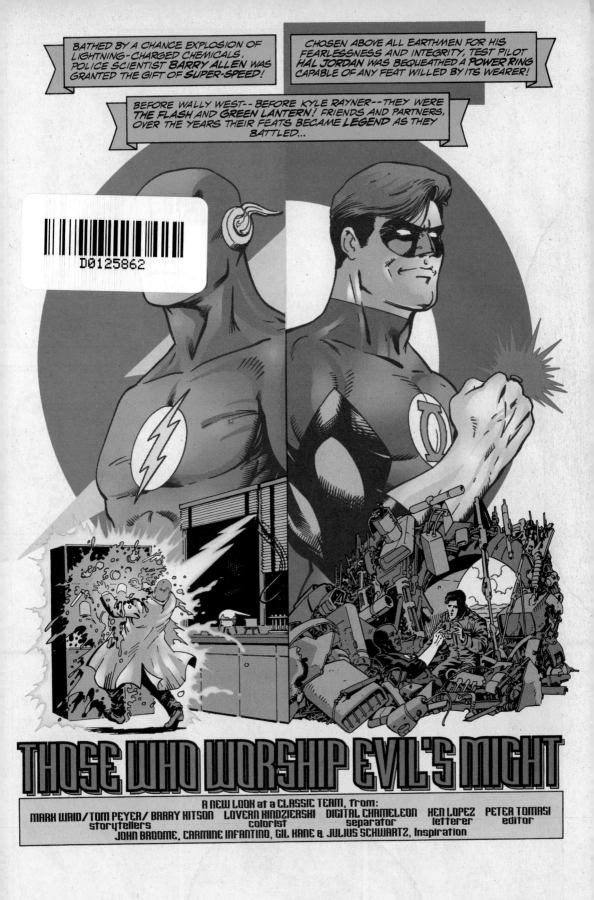

BATHED BY A CHANCE EXPLOSION OF LIGHTNING-CHARGED CHEMICALS, POLICE SCIENTIST *BARRY ALLEN* WAS GRANTED THE GIFT OF *SUPER-SPEED!*

CHOSEN ABOVE ALL EARTHMEN FOR HIS FEARLESSNESS AND INTEGRITY, TEST PILOT *HAL JORDAN* WAS BEQUEATHED A *POWER RING* CAPABLE OF ANY FEAT WILLED BY ITS WEARER!

BEFORE WALLY WEST-- BEFORE KYLE RAYNER-- THEY WERE THE *FLASH* AND *GREEN LANTERN!* FRIENDS AND PARTNERS, OVER THE YEARS THEIR FEATS BECAME *LEGEND* AS THEY BATTLED...

THOSE WHO WORSHIP EVIL'S MIGHT

A NEW LOOK at a CLASSIC TEAM, from:

MARK WAID / TOM PEYER / BARRY KITSON   LOVERN KINDZIERSKI   DIGITAL CHAMELEON   KEN LOPEZ   PETER TOMASI
storytellers   colorist   separator   letterer   editor

JOHN BROOME, CARMINE INFANTINO, GIL KANE & JULIUS SCHWARTZ, Inspiration

SEEMED LIKE SUCH A GOOD IDEA. BARRY AND I GET ALONG WELL AS *FLASH* AND *GREEN LANTERN* IN THE *JUSTICE LEAGUE.*

I THOUGHT IT'D BE FUN TO SEE IF WE COULD MAINTAIN THAT SAME CAMARADERIE *OFF* THE JOB.

I THOUGHT HE COULD FLY *OUT* FOR THE WEEKEND AND WE COULD *HANG.*

ALL OF THAT, OF COURSE, DEPENDED...

PHONES ☎ PUBLIC TELEPHONE

...ON BARRY ACTUALLY *SHOWING UP!*

--AND THAT'S *IT.* BUY YOU A *DRINK?*

SOUNDS GOOD.

GATE CLOSED

GATE CLOSED

CENTRAL CITY POLICE FORENSICS. BARRY ALLEN SPEAKING.

HAL? GOOD GOSH, WHAT *TIME* IS IT?

OH... THREE HOURS AFTER YOUR *PLANE* TOOK OFF.

CALL IRIS

HAL, I'M *SORRY!* THIS JOB'S JUST BURIED ME IN PAPERWORK--

HOW IS IT THE FASTEST MAN ALIVE IS ALWAYS LATE--

--UNLESS SOMEONE GETS THAT LEAD BUTT OF YOURS INTO *GEAR?*

CALL IRIS

WHO'S THE HUNK OF CHEESE ON HER ARM?

DIRK BOOSTROM. COMMERCIAL JET-JOCKEY. MY CURRENT COMPETITION.

I THOUGHT YOU WERE A TEST PILOT.

COMPETITION FOR CAROL. WHO ONLY HAS EYES FOR GREEN LANTERN. IT'S ALL VERY COMPLICATED.

...REFUSED TO WORRY ABOUT THE DANGER CAROL. I...

...I...

...I... CAN'T... LIE...!

THE TRUTH IS... I JUST WHIMPERED LIKE A BABY. I WAS PARALYZED WITH FEAR--AND THEN SOMETHING--WEIRD HAPPENED TO THE HIJACKER-- MENACING AND--

--DAAARRKK-KK-K!

AAAH!

HIS SHADOW! WHAT'S WITH HIS SHADOW?

HELP HIM!

SOMEBODY HELP HIM!

SO... EARTH'S *CHAMPIONS* HAVE COME TO *MEDDLE!* I WONDER IF YOU KNOW JUST WHAT IT IS YOU'RE DEFENDING?

SUPPOSE *YOU* TELL *US!*

ARE YOU BEHIND THAT *KILLER SHADOW?* WHO *ARE* YOU? WHAT DO YOU *WANT?*

I AM SCIENCE MINISTER SARAAR, AND ALL I WANT IS -- EARTH'S *EVIL!*

WHAAAT--?

WE *DORAGIANS* ARE SUFFERING UNDER A THREAT OF INVASION BY THE *KHUND* EMPIRE! WE ARE SUCH A *PLACID* PEOPLE THAT, TO MATCH THEIR AGGRESSION, WE MUST LOOK *OUTSIDE* OURSELVES!

MY *INFEKTIKON* TRANSMITS A PSI-VIRUS THAT LEECHES EVIL--AND DELIVERS IT HERE IN SHADOW FORM! SOON WE WILL REAP YOUR ENTIRE SUPPLY!

AT THE EXPENSE OF THE DONORS' LIVES?

SADLY. THE SHADOWS CANNOT SEPARATE FROM THEIR HOSTS WITHOUT FIRST SLAYING THEM.

YEAH? THEN I'D SAY YOU'RE ALREADY PRETTY *EVIL.*

THANK YOU... BUT WE CAN DO MUCH *BETTER.*

WHY NOT JUST LEECH IT FROM THE *KHUNDS?* THEY GET FRIENDLY, PROBLEM *SOLVED!*

YOU WOULDN'T BELIEVE THEIR *DEFENSES!* BESIDES, THERE'S AN OLD INTERPLANETARY ADAGE: "ACQUIRE FOOD FROM A *FARMER,* WORK FROM A *SLAVE--*

"--AND *CORRUPTION* FROM A *HUMAN!*" AAAHHHH-HAHA!!

YOU MONSTERS! YOU DOOMED MY WORLD AND YOU HAVEN'T COME CLOSE TO ENDING THE PLAGUE THAT WILL DESTROY YOUR OWN!

YEAH, YEAH.

COME ON, GL--

--LET'S MAKE THE WORLD SAFE FOR EVIL!

ALL RIGHT--

--BUT NOT THIS PARTICULAR EVIL!

LET'S SEE HOW THIS SHADOW LIKES A NOVA-BURST OF LIGHT!

NOT VERY MUCH.

SARAAR CALLED THIS A VIRUS--MEANING IT'S SPREADING LIKE A PLAGUE! BOOSTROM--CAN YOU TALK?

I--I'M NOT A VERY GOOD... NOT A VERY GOOD PERSON...

REMEMBER, HE SAID SOMETHING SIMILAR HAPPENED TO THE HIJACKER!

IF IT BEGAN WITH HIM...

WAS IT YOUR FLIGHT, THEN? IS THAT WHERE THIS STARTED?

HAD TO BE... PAN-TRANS... FLIGHT... 44...2...

I'LL RUSH HIM TO A HOSPITAL. MEET ME AT THE PAN-TRANS TERMINAL AS SOON AS YOU CAN.

ALL RIGHT. AND AS LONG AS WE'RE SPLITTING UP...

EH--?

BLAST IT! IN SAVING THE *OTHERS* -- WE EXPOSED *OURSELVES* TO THE *PLAGUE!*

SKASH

IF MY *RING* DIDN'T PROTECT ME FROM *MORTAL HARM,* I'D PROBABLY BE--

--DEAD.

SAME *SAVE...* ISN'T GONNA *WORK!* ITS *BEAM...* CAN *OVERWHELM* MINE! HE'S GOT... MORE *WILL...*

SWHOOM

DON'T *WORK* TOO WELL TOGETHER, DO THEY?

NO, AND I THINK AN IDEA OF *YOURS* MIGHT PUT AN END TO THIS...

...BUT I NEED *HELP.* I STILL DON'T FEEL ANY AGGRESSION AT *ALL.* I NEED TO *WANT* THIS.

I WAS JUST THINKING ABOUT THIS FAMOUS *QUOTE.* I'M BLANKING ON WHO *SAID* IT, BUT IT GOES...

"...IN ORDER FOR EVIL TO *TRIUMPH,* IT IS ONLY NECESSARY THAT GOOD MEN DO *NOTHING.*"

I *LIKE* THAT ONE!

FWAASH

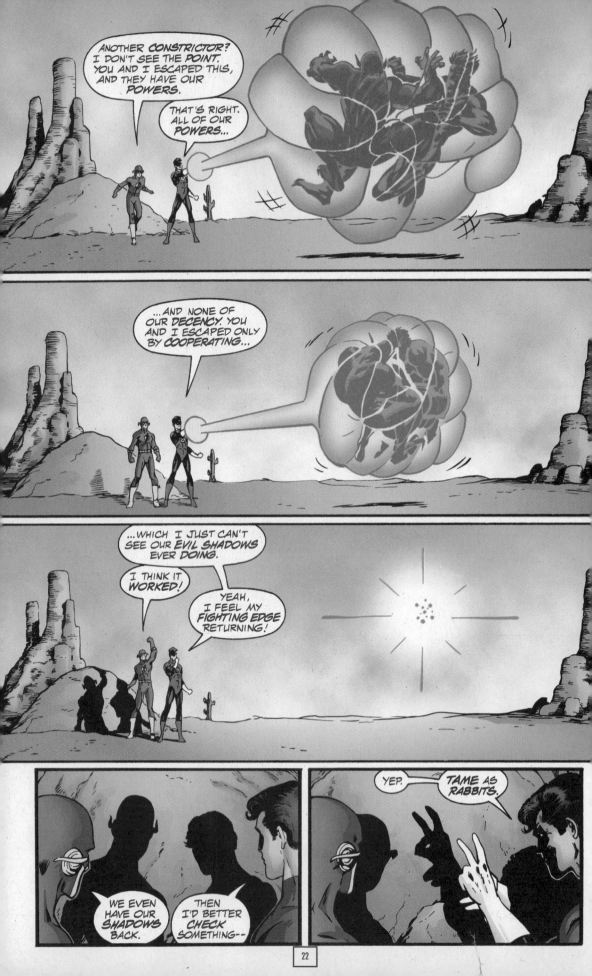

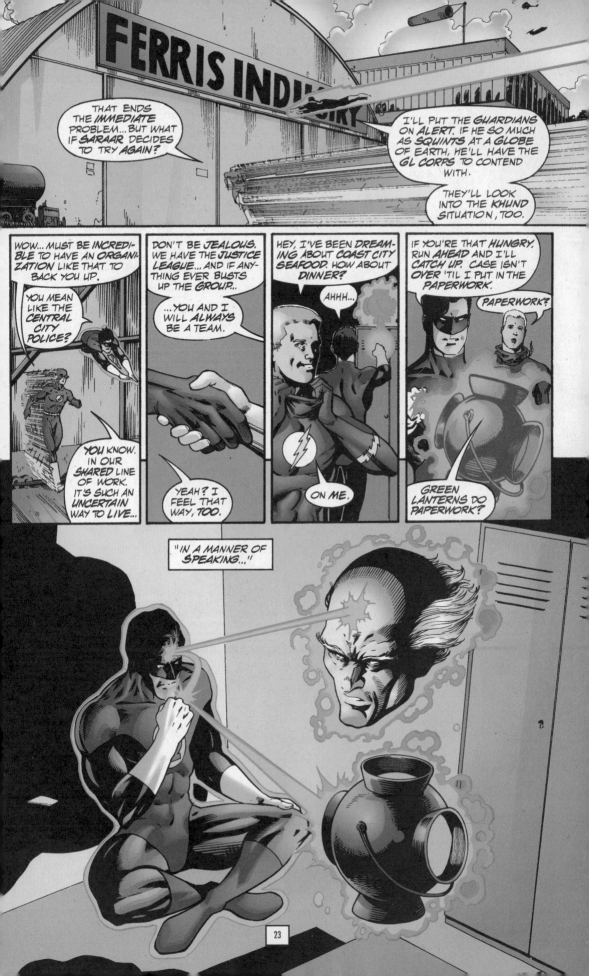

I SWEAR, I'LL PAY YOU BACK *QUICK* THIS TIME.

WORK IT OFF. I... *RAN* INTO SOMETHING ON THE *WAY* HERE THAT I THINK THE *THREE* OF US SHOULD INVESTIGATE.

HUH?

YOU KNOW. IN OUR *OTHER...*

...CLOTHES.

THREE OF US?

YOU MEAN *WALLY?* THEN HE'S--?

WELL, I'LL BE *DIPPED.*

WOW! YOU'RE GREEN LANTERN?

IS THAT AS COOL AS BEING A TEST PILOT?

COOLER!

MINUTES LATER...

...BANK ROBBERY FROM EARLY THIS MORNING. SOMETHING CUT A CLEAN HOLE IN THE SIDE OF THE VAULT. SOMETHING...

BANK

POLICE LINE D

...WITH A VERY FAMILIAR GREEN GLOW.

WAIT. YOU DON'T THINK I--?

OF COURSE NOT. QUESTION IS, WHO COULD DUPLICATE YOUR RING ENERGY THAT EFFECTIVELY?

WHO? A BELIEVER THAT IMITATION IS THE SINCEREST FORM--

NNNGH!

AAARGH!

FZZAK

FZZAK

--OF BATTERY!

31

HEY, LOOK AT ME, GL--

--I'M A CENTER FIELDER!

KNQR

PRETTY SHARP, KID!

HEY, FLASH! MY SIDEKICK JUST THOUGHT HIS WAY OUT OF A JAM ON HIS OWN! KID'S A NATURAL!

RIGHT! THOSE TWO CROOKS'RE NO MATCH FOR THE LANTERN-LANTERN TEAM!

BULLY FOR YOU.

SOMETHING WRONG, FLASH?

WE HAVEN'T CAUGHT ANYONE YET, KID FLASH... SO I WOULDN'T CELEBRATE--

≥SKRIIK≤

DISTURBANCE IN PROGRESS! MIRROR MASTER SIGHTED WITH UNIDENTIFIED ACCOMPLICE!

ALL UNITS TO CENTRAL CITY ARENA!

C'MON, SON! LET'S TEACH THOSE GUYS A LESSON!

YIPPEE!

...AND SO THE AMBASSADOR TO FRANCE JUST WOULDN'T STOP PESTERING ME FOR DATES. I FINALLY HAD TO *SAY* TO HIM, "MR. AMBASSADOR, HONEY--"

I WONDER WHAT'S KEEPING BARRY AND HAL?

BARRY AND HAL... NOW *THEY'RE* A PAIR... WHATEVER *DO* THEY *SEE* IN EACH OTHER?

WHAT DOES *HAL* SEE IN YOU, LADY?

FOR *THAT* MATTER, WHAT DO I SEE IN *BARRY?*

I DON'T *GET* IT, THOUGH. ALL THIS *HAVOC*, AND YET THE BAD GUYS ACCOMPLISHED VERY *LITTLE* IN TERMS OF *PERSONAL GAIN*...

THAT'S THE *THING* ABOUT YOUR VILLAINS. THEY COMMIT CRIMES TO BOOST THEIR *EGOS* MORE THAN THEIR *BANKROLLS*, DON'T THEY?

IT'S ALMOST LIKE A BIG *MACABRE GAME* TO THEM...

SO FAR. LET'S HOPE IT *STAYS* THAT WAY. OTHERWISE WALLY'S GOING TO HAVE HIS *HANDS* FULL IN THE YEARS *AHEAD*.

ME?

SURE. WHO *ELSE* IS GOING TO FILL MY *BOOTS* WHEN I'M RESTING IN SOME NICE *RETIREMENT HOME* SOMEWHERE?

YOU'RE *ITCHING* FOR SOME *AUTOGRAPHS*. I CAN TELL. *GO.*

CLEVER *BOY*. LISTEN...ABOUT *EARLIER*... I DIDN'T WANT TO SAY ANYTHING IN FRONT OF *WALLY*, BUT I CAME ON A LITTLE *HARSH*.

IF I'D GIVEN YOU THE BENEFIT OF THE *DOUBT*, I WOULDN'T HAVE GOTTEN *DISTRACTED*—WHICH COST US *BIG*.

DON'T APOLOGIZE. INTENTIONAL OR *NOT*, I CUT YOU OFF AT THE *KNEES* IN FRONT OF YOUR OWN *NEPHEW*. CAN'T *BLAME* YOU FOR BEING STEAMED.

GOOD THING HE GOT US OUT OF THE *TRAP*. WONDER WHY HE DIDN'T JUST USE HIS *RING* TO STOP IT BEFORE IT *CAUGHT* US?

WHO KNOWS? I'D LIKE TO *BELIEVE* THAT HE SAVED US WITH *SUPER-SPEED* JUST TO REMIND ME WHERE HIS *HEART* REALLY WAS...

...BUT I DON'T KNOW THAT EVEN HE'S *THAT* GOOD.

46

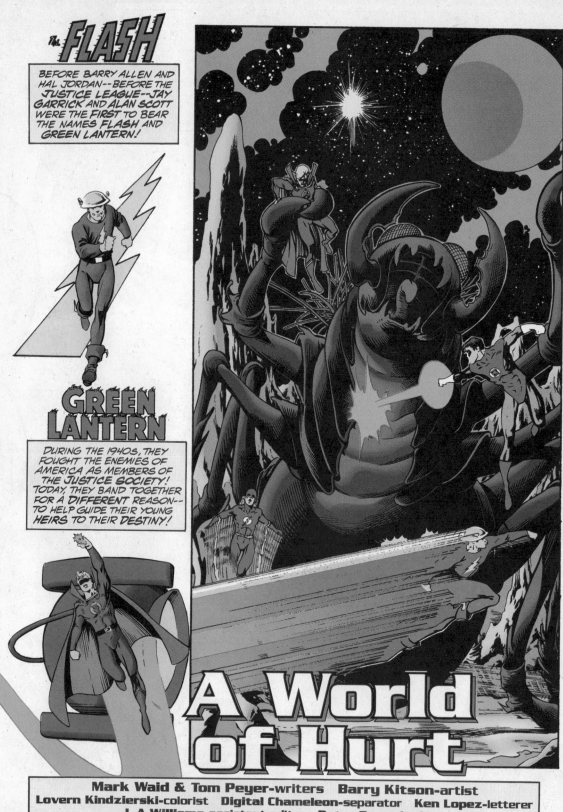

The FLASH

BEFORE BARRY ALLEN AND HAL JORDAN--BEFORE THE JUSTICE LEAGUE--JAY GARRICK AND ALAN SCOTT WERE THE FIRST TO BEAR THE NAMES FLASH AND GREEN LANTERN!

GREEN LANTERN

DURING THE 1940s, THEY FOUGHT THE ENEMIES OF AMERICA AS MEMBERS OF THE JUSTICE SOCIETY! TODAY, THEY BAND TOGETHER FOR A *DIFFERENT* REASON-- TO HELP GUIDE THEIR YOUNG HEIRS TO THEIR DESTINY!

A World of Hurt

Mark Waid & Tom Peyer-writers **Barry Kitson**-artist
Lovern Kindzierski-colorist **Digital Chameleon**-separator **Ken Lopez**-letterer
L.A. Williams-assistant editor **Peter Tomasi**-editor

SPLOOK

WHAT IN THE NAME OF--?

WHAT'S GOING ON, HERE?

YOU PICKED A BAD SPOT TO PITCH THE TENT.

RIGHT. THIS PLANET. NOTICE HOW ITS NATURAL QUIRKS SEEM TO BE TAILORED TO OUR WEAKNESSES? LIKE IT HAS IT IN FOR US PERSONALLY?

WELL, THE DESERT SURE SEEMS TO.

I SAY WE MOVE CAMP TO THAT WOODED AREA WE CAME IN ON.

I DON'T KNOW, BARRY. WOOD'S ALAN'S WEAKNESS. IF NATURE HAS ANY MORE SURPRISES FOR US--

I SAY BRING THEM ON! GREEN LANTERNS AREN'T AFRAID OF A LITTLE HARDSHIP... ARE WE, HAL?

ALAN...

...I'M NOT AFRAID OF ANYTHING!

SIXTY YEARS INTO THE MODERN HEROIC AGE, MASKED CRUSADERS REPRESENT SOMETHING *DEEPER* THAN AWE-INSPIRING PHENOMENA--THEY EMBODY *LEGACIES!*

BEFORE KYLE RAYNER, TEST PILOT *HAL JORDAN* HELD THE ROLE OF THE WILL-POWERED DEFENDER OF THE COSMOS, *GREEN LANTERN!*

BEFORE WALLY WEST, POLICE SCIENTIST *BARRY ALLEN* WORE THE MANTLE OF THE FASTEST MAN ALIVE, *THE FLASH!*

BEFORE CONNOR HAWKE, ACTIVIST *OLIVER QUEEN* FOUGHT FOR THE COMMON GOOD AS *GREEN ARROW!*

GREEN ARROW! HAVE YOU GONE *NUTS?* THOSE ARE CENTRAL CITY'S MOST *DANGEROUS* VILLAINS--

--AND YOU'RE SETTING THEM *FREE!*

THEY LIVE FOREVER IN OUR HEARTS, WHERE THE IMPULSES OF *NOSTALGIA* PROMPT US TO REGARD THEIR BYGONE DAYS AS A *SIMPLER TIME.*

WE COULDN'T BE MORE *WRONG.*

WAKE *UP,* BOY SCOUTS--THE *REVOLUTION* IS HERE!

HOW MANY TIMES CAN A MAN TURN HIS HEAD?

MARK WAID and TOM PEYER, writers   TOM GRINDBERG, penciller   BARRY KITSON, inker   LOVERN KINDZIERSKI, colorist   DIGITAL CHAMELEON, separator   KEN LOPEZ, letterer   L.A. WILLIAMS, assistant editor   PETER TOMASI, editor   For DENNY and NEAL

I JUST WISH PHIST WEREN'T USING IT TO KNOCK *ME.*

BARRY, HONEY, DON'T TAKE IT *PERSONALLY.* CENTRAL CITY'S ALWAYS *SWARMED* WITH SUPER-VILLAINS...

...AND THERE'S ONLY SO MUCH EVEN THE *FLASH* CAN DO TO KEEP THEM *ALL* AT BAY.

ME, I'M *GRATEFUL* FOR THE *ASSIST.* NOT ONLY ARE YOU GETTING THE *DOWN TIME* TO HELP AROUND THE *HOUSE...*

OH!

...BUT *I'M* GETTING A LOT LESS FLASH AND A LOT MORE BARRY ALLEN!

LOOK, IF YOU'RE *BORED,* CALL ONE OF YOUR *FRIENDS.* RALPH'S ALWAYS FUN, AND *HAL*--

NOT HAL.

WHY NOT? COME TO *THINK* OF IT, WE HAVEN'T SEEN *HIM* IN *MONTHS!* IS THERE SOME *REASON* YOU TWO STOPPED HANGING *OUT?*

NO... NO...

SO I FORGOT TO SEND IN THE RENEWAL! GUESS I GOT SIDE-TRACKED DEALING WITH *TRIVIA* LIKE *POVERTY* AND THE *DRUG PLAGUE!*

GO SOLVE A *REAL* CRIME, YOU *NAZI!* I'LL PAY A FINE-- BUT YOU'RE NOT *ABOUT* TO JAIL ME OVER A PAPER-WORK SNAFU!

OLLIE, THE LAW'S THE LAW! CALM DOWN AND WE'LL--

SIR, RESISTING ARREST IS UNACCEPTABLE.

HEY! THERE'S NO CALL FOR *THAT!* DROP YOUR *WEAPON* BEFORE I--

SIR, RESISTING ARREST IS UNACCEPTABLE.

SWOK

...LIFE IS LESS HECTIC FOR *FLASH,* THAT'S *TRUE...*

...BUT I CAN'T HELP GETTING A *BAD VIBE* OFF THE NEW ADMINISTRATION! HOW CAN YOU *TRUST* A POLICEMAN IF YOU CAN'T SEE HIS *FACE?*

STILL, SOME THINK THEY'RE DOING THE *JOB* SO LONG AS THEY'RE CLEANING THE STREETS OF CRIMINALS LIKE--

--HAL JORDAN?

79

DON'T TALK ABOUT ME AS IF I'M NOT HERE, OLLIE!

NOT EVERYTHING'S AS BLACK AND WHITE AS THEY'D WANT YOU TO BELIEVE, PAL!

I'M SHOWING YOU THE *REAL* WORLD FOR THE FIRST TIME! "FORGET ABOUT CHASING AROUND THE *GALAXY*," I TOLD YOU! "LOOK AT *AMERICA*-- HARD!"

YOU'RE *NOT* HERE! YOU'RE *DANGLING* FROM THE *STRINGS* OF ALIEN *PUPPETEERS*.

SO YOU'RE GIVING HIM YOUR *SELECTIVE GUIDED TOUR*. WHAT DO YOU DO, BREEZE INTO A TOWN AND SAVE THE POOR, INCOMPETENT LOCALS FROM *THEMSELVES*?

YOU'RE NOT *HEARING* ME! I JUST WANT TO SHOW HIM WHAT ONE MAN CAN *DO*! THIS IS A *GOOD* COUNTRY! BEAUTIFUL... FERTILE... AND *TERRIBLY SICK*!

FATCATS DUMP *SEWAGE* INTO OUR *RIVERS*! KIDS PUMP *POISON* INTO THEIR VEINS FOR A *CHEAP HIGH*! MOTHERS GO WITHOUT SO THEIR KIDS CAN *EAT*!

THOSE ARE THE REAL CRIMES IN AMERICA, ALLEN--NOT THE *JAY-WALKING* YOUR BADGE-WIELDING *YAHOOS* BREAK HEADS OVER!

I LIKED *EVE DOREMUS* BETTER.

LISTEN, BARRY...

NO! YOU LISTEN TO ME! THE POLICE KEEP THE *ORDER* IN THIS TOWN--

--WITH *STEEL TRUNCHEONS*--

--AND IF YOU'D COME DOWN OFF YOUR *PERCH*, YOU'D *REMEMBER* THEY DON'T HAVE *TRICK ARROWS* OR *POWER RINGS* LIKE... SOME PEOPLE!

THEY'RE *MORTAL MEN* ON THE *LINE* IN A DANGEROUS *CITY*!

AND THEY'RE JUST FOLLOWING *ORDERS*, RIGHT?

NO ONE'S *SAYING* COPS ARE *BAD*, SWIFTY--BUT THEY'RE NOT *GODS*, EITHER! THEY'VE GOTTA BE *WATCHED*!

YOU THINK I HAVEN'T HAD MY *ANTENNAE* UP? I *AM* WATCHING! AND I'M *WORRIED*!

THEN THAT'S NOT WHAT'S REALLY *BOTHERING YOU*, IS IT?

82

MAYOR D. PHIST

--ALWAYS HAPPY TO VISIT WITH MY FELLOW *CRIMEBUSTERS!* MARGIE-- HOLD MY *CALLS!*

CIGARS, GENTLEMEN?

NO *THANKS!* IF I WANT TO POISON MY *LUNGS,* I CAN TAKE A WHIFF OF THE *TOXIC WASTE* YOU BUILT YOUR *PLATFORM* ON!

LAW AND *ORDER?* WHEN DID YOU *LONGJOHN* TYPES GO SOFT ON *CRIME?*

TRUST ME! WE ARE *ALL* ON THE *SAME SIDE* HERE!

FLASH, YOU'RE A *FRIEND* OF THIS ADMINISTRATION--!

SO LONG AS *IT* STAYS *FRIENDLY,* MAYOR--AND *FRIENDSHIP'S* NOT THE *PREVALENT ATTITUDE* IN *CENTRAL* THESE DAYS!

UNLIKE *YOU,* I WAS *ELECTED--*

--BY DECENT, *MIDDLE-CLASS* FAMILIES WHO *DESERVE* TO ENJOY THE FRUITS OF THEIR HONEST LABORS WITHOUT BEING *ATOMIZED* BY KILLER BOOMERANGS OR TRAPPED IN MIRRORS!

HAVE YOU FLIPPED YOUR *BIRD?* A TOWN THAT'D TRADE *FREEDOM* FOR *SECURITY* IS LIVING A PARANOID *DELUSION!*

THAT'S NOT A *DREAM,* BROTHER--THAT'S A *NIGHTMARE!*

AH, YES! POUR ME SOME *LIBERAL WHINE!* THESE ARE *TOUGH TIMES,* FLASH-- AND I BRING *TOUGH MEASURES!*

SPARE ME YOUR *ARROGANCE!* MY PEOPLE *UNDERSTAND* WHAT I'M GIVING THEM--AND THEY'RE HUNGRY FOR PEACE AT *ANY PRICE!* SO IF YOU'LL *EXCUSE* ME--

SLAM

THAT WENT WELL.

THIS STINKS ON *ICE!* WHAT DOES THAT *JACKASS* THINK HE'S GETTING *AWAY* WITH?

PROJECT: REHAB.

EXCUSE ME?

I ONLY GOT A *GLANCE*-- BUT IT HAD *SOMETHING* TO DO WITH HIS *NEXT* PHASE OF CRIME CONTROL.

YOU SNUCK HIS *FILES* OUT? AND HE DIDN'T *NOTICE?*

I WAS COUNTING ON YOU MAKING A *SCENE.* THANKS FOR NOT LETTING ME *DOWN.*

I DON'T BELIEVE IT! THIS IS *AMERICA!* PHIST CAN'T BE DOING THIS...!

ONE WAY TO KNOW FOR *SURE.* IF THIS IS *TRUE,* THEN YOUR *ROGUES* ARE NO LONGER SNUG IN THEIR CELLS.

YOU'RE RIGHT. THEY'RE GONE.

PHIST CALLED US *"CRIMEBUSTERS"?* FINE.

THEN LET'S START *BUSTING.*

86

NOW I AM.

SKRAAAK!

I CAN'T *WAIT* TO HEAR YOU EXPLAIN THIS TO THE *JUSTICE DEPARTMENT*, PHIST.

WE'VE GOT RECORDS ON *ALL* YOUR *ILLEGAL ACTIVITIES!* YOU'LL GO TO *PRISON...* AND YOU'LL *ROT!*

UH-OH.

I *SPRUNG* 'EM-- I FIGURE IT'S *MY* JOB TO PUT 'EM BACK IN THE *JUG!* YOU TWO TAKE CARE OF *PHIST!* THEN--

--I DON'T *KNOW*-- GO GRAB A *BEER* AND A COUPLE OF *FISHING POLES*, FOR CRYIN' OUT LOUD!

NOT SO FAST, TWINKLETOES!

YOU'RE LETTING THEM *GO*? SURE, THEY'VE *SUFFERED*, BUT--

DON'T GET YOUR *SOCKS* IN A KNOT, GRANDMA! WHAT DO YOU THINK *I* AM, A *FANATIC*?

Picture Ne

Central City

Since 1899

15¢

Ap

MAYOR ARRESTE

Mayor Deuteronomy Phist en route to answer charges of felony prisoner abuse. The officers pictured were the first to revert to old low-tech uniforms.
(Photo by Iris Allen)

LexCorp Recalls Tech

Green Arrow Rounds Up Escaped Rogues

-- FIGURE BETWEEN PHIST HEADED FOR *TRIAL* AND THE POLICE DEPARTMENT *RESTRUCTURING*, NEITHER IRIS NOR I WILL BE *HOME* MUCH THIS WEEK.

YOU TWO WOULD HAVE OUR PLACE PRETTY MUCH TO *YOURSELVES* IF YOU WANT TO STAY...

THANKS FOR THE *GLAD HAND*, RED... BUT I JUST GOT A *BETTER* OFFER. NO OFFENSE.

SALE

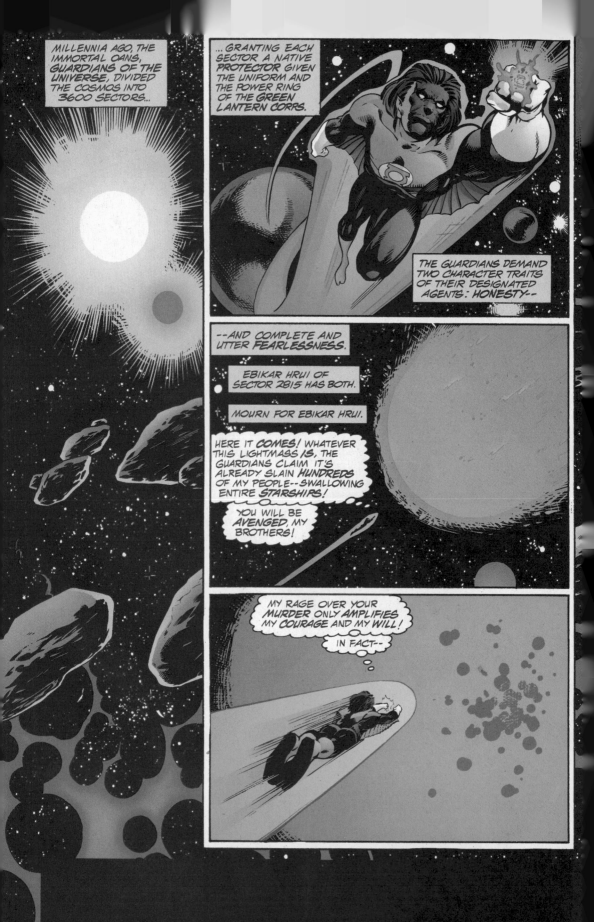

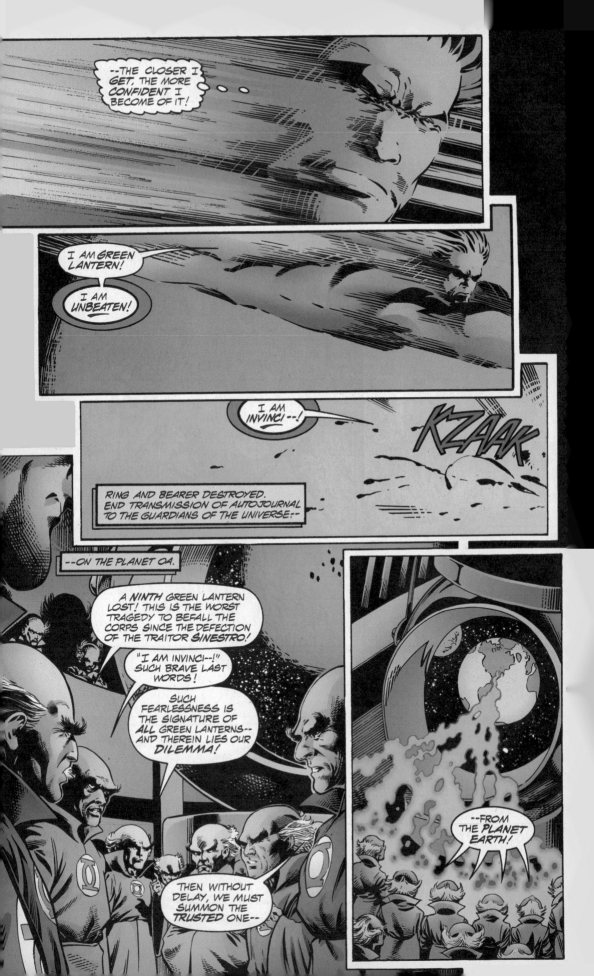

IT'S A RED-LETTER DAY! LIGHT WORKLOAD AT THE LAB FOR *BARRY ALLEN*, AND NO CRIMINALS LOOSE IN CENTRAL CITY FOR *THE FLASH* TO ROUND UP!

I CAN'T *WAIT* TO SEE THE LOOK ON IRIS' FACE WHEN I SHOW UP *ON TIME!*

DINNER'S READY! THAT MEANS BARRY SHOULD BE HOME WITHIN THE *HOUR*...OR TWO, OR *THREE*...

HONESTLY, WHY DO I EVEN *BOTHER?*

BECAUSE YOU WERE LUCKY ENOUGH TO MARRY THE MAN OF YOUR *DREAMS?*

BARRY! I DON'T *BELIEVE* IT! YOU'RE ON--

VIZZHHT!

BARRY?!

BEFORE KYLE RAYNER, TRUCK DRIVER HAL JORDAN SERVED IN AN INTER-GALACTIC CORPS OF HEROES WHO WORE THE POWER RING AND THE NAME OF GREEN LANTERN!

BEFORE WALLY WEST, POLICE SCIENTIST BARRY ALLEN SUSTAINED THE LEGACY OF THE FASTEST MAN ALIVE, THE FLASH!

THEY WERE FELLOW JUSTICE LEAGUERS... BEST FRIENDS... AND EVEN RIVALS, ON THE DAY THE LEADERS OF THE CORPS TRANSFERRED THEIR TRUST TO...

THE MAN WITHOUT FEARLESSNESS!

MARK WAID and TOM PEYER–WRITERS

BARRY KITSON–ARTIST

KEN LOPEZ–LETTERER

LOVERN KINDZIERSKI–COLORIST

DIGITAL CHAMELEON–SEPS

L.A. WILLIAMS–ASSISTANT EDITOR

PETER TOMASI–EDITOR

--GOSH!

FLASH OF EARTH! LISTEN CAREFULLY! WE NEED YOUR HELP!

YOU MAY BE THE ONLY HERO LEFT WHO CAN SAVE THE GREEN LANTERN CORPS...

...FROM TOTAL ANNIHILATION!

I'M **FLATTERED**, SIRS... BUT DON'T YOU NORMALLY CONSULT **HAL JORDAN** IN A CRISIS?

YOUR SECTOR'S GREEN LANTERN MUST **NEVER** KNOW WE SUMMONED **YOU!**

WELL... THAT COULD BE AWKWARD, SIR. HAL AND I ARE **VERY** CLOSE FRIENDS.

DO YOU WANT HIM TO **DIE?**

DIE? MAYBE YOU'D BETTER **TELL** ME WHAT THIS IS **ABOUT?**

A BLISTERING LIGHT OF **FINALITY** IS PASSING OVER CREATION-- ACTIVELY SEARCHING OUT AND **DESTROYING** SENTIENT LIFEFORMS! WE CANNOT ASCERTAIN THE **ORIGIN** OF THIS ROGUE STAR, NOR WHAT MAY BE **GUIDING** IT...

...BUT IT SEEMS TO **PROTECT** ITSELF BY AMPLIFYING THE **PERSONALITY TRAITS** OF ITS **VICTIMS!** THE TIMID BECOME **COWARDS,** THE ANGRY BECOME **BERSERK...**

...AND THE **FEARLESS** BECOME **FOOLHARDY,** PLUNGING HEADLONG INTO AN ENERGY CORE CAPABLE OF **ANNIHILATING** EVEN THOSE WHOSE RINGS NORMALLY PROTECT THEM FROM **MORTAL HARM!**

I SEE WHERE THIS IS **GOING.** THEY DON'T COME MORE FEARLESS THAN **HAL,** DO THEY?

EXACTLY. **EVERY** GREEN LANTERN SLAIN THUS FAR, EVEN THOSE **FOREWARNED,** LOST ALL SENSE OF **SELF-PRESERVATION** THE MOMENT THEY CAME WITHIN RANGE OF THE STAR'S **EFFECTS.**

JORDAN WOULD SIMPLY BE ANOTHER BODY ON THE PYRE...

...BUT TRY TELLING **HIM** THAT. I UNDERSTAND. SO...

102

THE MAN WITHOUT FEARLESSNESS! PART TWO

THE GUARDIANS SAID NOT TO WORRY ABOUT TAKING DIRECT ACTION-- TO CONCENTRATE ON RECONNAISSANCE.

THEY FIGURED THAT ONLY *I'D* BE FAST ENOUGH TO ESCAPE WHATEVER'S AT THE *CORE* OF THIS STAR!

WHEW! THE CLOSER I COME TO THE CENTER, THE HOTTER IT *GETS!* BETWEEN MY OWN FRICTION-SHIELD AURA AND THE GUARDIANS' *BIOSHEATH*, I SHOULD BE PROTECTED! WHY...?

...

OH, MY *GOD*--!

HAL JORDAN? WHAT BRINGS *YOU* TO OA? WE DID NOT SUMMON YOU.

BUT PERHAPS YOU *DID* SUMMON A *FRIEND* OF MINE. RED SUIT, WINGS ON HIS EARS... HAVE YOU SEEN HIM?

YOU WOULD QUESTION *US*?

ON BEHALF OF HIS WIFE... HIS *MATE*...YES. AND THAT DIDN'T SOUND MUCH LIKE A "NO."

YOUR CONCERN FOR YOUR FRIEND IS... *MISPLACED*, GREEN LANTERN OF SECTOR 2814.

I *SEE*. GUESS I'M ON THE WRONG TRAIL, THEN. IF YOU DON'T MIND, I'LL JUST RECHARGE MY *RING* BEFORE I GO...

NO!!

GET *OUT* OF HERE!

YOU'RE *WELCOME.*

I MEAN IT! THIS THING'S *ALREADY* WIPED OUT *NINE* GREEN LANTERNS!

NINE--?

THEN STAY HERE WHERE IT'S *SAFE,* ITTY--

--BECAUSE WE LANTERNS TAKE CARE OF OUR *OWN!*

HAL, *WAIT*--

I SAID

WAIT!

BARRY, I APPRECIATE YOUR CONCERN, BUT QUIT TRYING TO *PROTECT* ME! I'M NOT *AFRAID* OF THIS THING!

NO GREEN LANTERN COULD BE! THAT'S THE *PROBLEM!*

WHATEVER YOU COME *AT* IT WITH, IT *AMPS!* IT TURNS YOUR *BRAVERY* INTO *RECKLESSNESS*-- CRIPPLING ANY SENSE OF *SELF-PRESERVATION!*

THAT'S HOW IT *WINS*-- BY LURING GREEN LANTERNS IN *HEADLONG!*

INTO *WHAT?*

YOU WANT TO SEE?

108

FINE.

THIS ENERGY CONSTRUCT IS LIKE A MINIATURE *SUN*... ONE THAT GLOWS *ORANGE*... BUT ONLY ON THE *OUTSIDE.*

INSIDE, HOWEVER MUCH IT BENDS THE LAWS OF *ASTROPHYSICS*, IT BURNS *HOTTER*... ONE STEP *UP* THE SPECTRUM.

IT BURNS *YELLOW*... THE ONE *COLOR,* HAL...

THAT THE GLS ARE POWERLESS *AGAINST.*

THAT'S...THAT'S WHAT YOU WERE *SAVING* ME FROM...

DOESN'T *MATTER.* LET ME *AT* IT! I'LL KICK IT FROM HERE TO *RANN!*

LISTEN TO YOURSELF! GET A GRIP! IF WE'RE GOING TO DO ANYTHING, WE'RE GOING TO HAVE TO DO IT *TOGETHER*--

--BUT WE'RE *DOUBLY CRIPPLED*--BECAUSE FOR SOME REASON, I CAN'T SEEM TO HIT *TOP SPEED* WHEN I'M NEAR THIS THING!

I THOUGHT IT WAS SUPPOSED TO *AMPLIFY* PERSONAL TRAITS!

AND IT *DOES!* DON'T YOU *SEE?*

THOSE SMUG--! THE GUARDIANS DON'T *KNOW* YOU LIKE I DO! THEY ALMOST GOT YOU *KILLED!*

THE FLASH MAY BE THE FASTEST MAN ALIVE--

--BUT *BARRY ALLEN* IS SLOWER THAN *MOLASSES!* THAT'S THE WEAKNESS THIS THING IS *EXPLOITING!*

HAL, *STOP!*

GOOD *CALL!* KEEP THINKING THAT *CLEARLY,* AND WE STAND A *CHANCE!*

I'M THINKING *FAST* AGAIN--AND I'VE GOT AN *IDEA!* WORK WITH ME!

WE STAY *OUTSIDE!* I CIRCLE IT

AS FAST AS I *CAN,* CREATING

A *"SOLAR WIND"* OF LOOSE

HYDROGEN ATOMS--

AND?

110

RUNNING ON empty

MARK WAID/TOM PEYER/BARRY KITSON, storytellers
LOVERN KINDZIERSKI, colorist DIGITAL CHAMELEON, separator KEN LOPEZ, letterer
L.A. WILLIAMS, assistant editor PETER TOMASI, editor Special thanks to ROB FRENAY

For JOHN BROOME

WELL, *THAT* SEEMED TO SNAP BARRY *TO*. MAYBE I'M WORRIED OVER *NOTHING*.

THE SECOND *TROUBLE* APPEARS, HE PITCHES RIGHT *IN* AND DOES HIS *WORK*, LIKE EVERYTHING'S *JAKE*. I'M ALMOST *GRATEFUL* THE TOWER--

--THE TOWER! OH, *GOD*-- I JUST REMEMBERED!

IS THERE A *CONNECTION?* THERE'S GOT TO BE! *PIE* KNOWS--!

FLASH! I HAVE TO TELL YOU! IT'S ABOUT THE TOWER--

FLASH, *PLEASE!*

IT'S IMPOR--

FAASH!

≈UNNH!≈

126

≥HHHNNH≤

RING, HOW IS HE?

SCAN REVEALS NO INTERNAL DAMAGE. SUBJECT IS REGAINING CONSCIOUSNESS.

PIE? CAN YOU HEAR ME? WHAT HIT YOU?

HAL! WHERE'S CAROL?

MISSING.

AND THE SAPPHIRE?

ALSO GONE. SHE WAS THE ONE WHO ATTACKED YOU, WASN'T SHE?

I DIDN'T SEE, BUT I'D GUESS. WHAT ARE WE GOING TO DO?

YOU'RE GOING HOME TO TERGA AND THE KIDS. IF... SHE'S BACK, I WANT YOU OUT OF THE LINE OF FIRE.

"SHE"? WHO'S "SHE"?

CAROL. OR, RATHER...

...STAR SAPPHIRE.

CAROL DOESN'T KNOW IT, BUT SHE LEADS A DUAL LIFE. SHE WAS ONCE APPOINTED QUEEN OF A MAN-HATING RACE CALLED THE ZAMARONS... AND CROWNED WITH A SUPER-POWERFUL SAPPHIRE GEM.

WHENEVER SHE COMES IN CONTACT WITH IT, SHE'S POSSESSED BY THAT IDENTITY. LAST TIME I STOPPED HER, I BURIED THE GEM UNDER THAT TOWER TO KEEP HER CLEAR OF IT.

IT LOOKS LIKE SOMEONE WANTS HER TO HAVE IT.

DID YOU SAY... STAR SAPPHIRE?

YEAH. SOMETHING ODD ABOUT THAT?

RUNNING ON empty

SHE *WOULD* HAVE TO SHOOT *YELLOW* ENERGY! SHE KNOWS MY RING'S *USELESS* AGAINST THAT COLOR!

FLASH! TAKE PIE--

--ANYWHERE ELSE!

FWOOSH

I KNOW!

WHAT IS IT YOU *WANT*, CAROL?

THIS *AGAIN?*

I AM NOT "CAROL."

WHO DUG THE *SAPPHIRE* OUT FOR YOU, CAROL?

WHO'S *USING* YOU? THE *ZAMARONS?*

THAT I'M *INCAPABLE* OF ACTING ON MY *OWN?*

IS *THAT* WHAT YOU *THINK?*

SHZAAAK

FLASH, SOMETHING'S REALLY *WRONG!* I'VE NEVER SEEN HER SO ANGRY... SO POINT-LESSLY *DESTRUCTIVE!*

YEAH, WELL...

...THERE'S A LOT OF THAT GOING *AROUND!*

129

CAROL! CAROL, CAN YOU *HEAR* ME?

GREEN LANTERN? WHAT-- WHAT'S HAPPENING?

EASY, EVERYTHING'S ALL *RIGHT* NOW.

NOT QUITE, I'M AFRAID. I CAN'T FIND THE *OTHER* SAPPHIRE.

WE'LL SEARCH THE AREA, BUT *FIRST*... BEFORE SHE GETS HER HANDS ON THIS GEMSTONE...

ONE MORE THING. BACK *THERE*... I'M SORRY I... I LOST MY GRIP...

I MISS IRIS *SO* MUCH... BUT SHE'D BE *GLAD* TO... TO KNOW I HAD SOMEBODY AROUND TO SET ME *STRAIGHT*... WHEN I *NEEDED* IT.

ANYTIME. AFTER ALL, PAL...

...WHAT ARE FRIENDS *FOR*?

...I'M GOING TO BURY IT *DEEP*.

141

SOON THE FLASH WOULD FACE HIS ULTIMATE CRISIS, SHEDDING HIS LAST BLOOD FOR THE UNIVERSE.

YEARS LATER, AND BY A MORE TORTUOUS ROUTE, GREEN LANTERN WOULD BRAVELY MEET HIS OWN END.

TWO MEN GONE, ONE ETERNAL BOND. I STILL FEEL IT. HEAR IT.

THEIR ENDLESS TALK, OBSESSIVELY COMPARING THE SMALLEST DETAILS, A WAY OF KEEPING SCORE.

HAL'S FASCINATION WITH THE FLASH'S FREEDOM AND BARRY ALLEN'S DISCIPLINE.

BARRY'S FASCINATION WITH GREEN LANTERN'S DISCIPLINE AND HAL JORDAN'S FREEDOM.

I HEAR BARRY PRYING INTO HAL'S LOVE LIFE, AND HAL PRYING ANOTHER TWENTY-DOLLAR LOAN TO BE REPAID... SOMETIME. NO HURRY. THEY'D HAVE THEIR WHOLE LIVES TO EVEN THINGS OUT.

AND TURNING AWAY, THEY MAP THEIR SEPARATE ROUTES BY THE SETTING SUN AND BOLDLY LAUNCH THEMSELVES...

THEY JOKE, MAKE PLANS, AND PUNCH EACH OTHER'S SHOULDERS, AN AWKWARD SCHOOLBOY GOODBYE.

THE STARS OF THE
DC UNIVERSE
CAN ALSO BE FOUND IN THESE BOOKS:

TO FIND MORE COLLECTED EDITIONS AND MONTHLY COMIC BOOKS FROM DC COMICS,
CALL 1-888-COMIC BOOK FOR THE NEAREST COMICS SHOP OR GO TO YOUR LOCAL BOOK STORE.

Visit us at www.dccomics.com